The Magic School Bus

Inside a Hurricane

The Magic School Bus
Inside a Hurricane

By Joanna Cole
Illustrated by Bruce Degen

Scholastic Inc.
New York · Toronto · London · Auckland · Sydney
Mexico City · New Delhi · Hong Kong · Buenos Aires

The author and illustrator wish to thank Dr. Robert C. Sheets,
Director of the National Hurricane Center, and Dr. Daniel Leathers,
Delaware State Climatologist, University of Delaware,
for their assistance in preparing this book.

ISBN-13: 978-0-590-44687-7
ISBN-10: 0-590-44687-8

40 39 38 37   12 1 14 15/0

Printed in the U.S.A.   40

The illustrator used pen and ink, watercolor, color pencil,
and gouache for the paintings in this book.

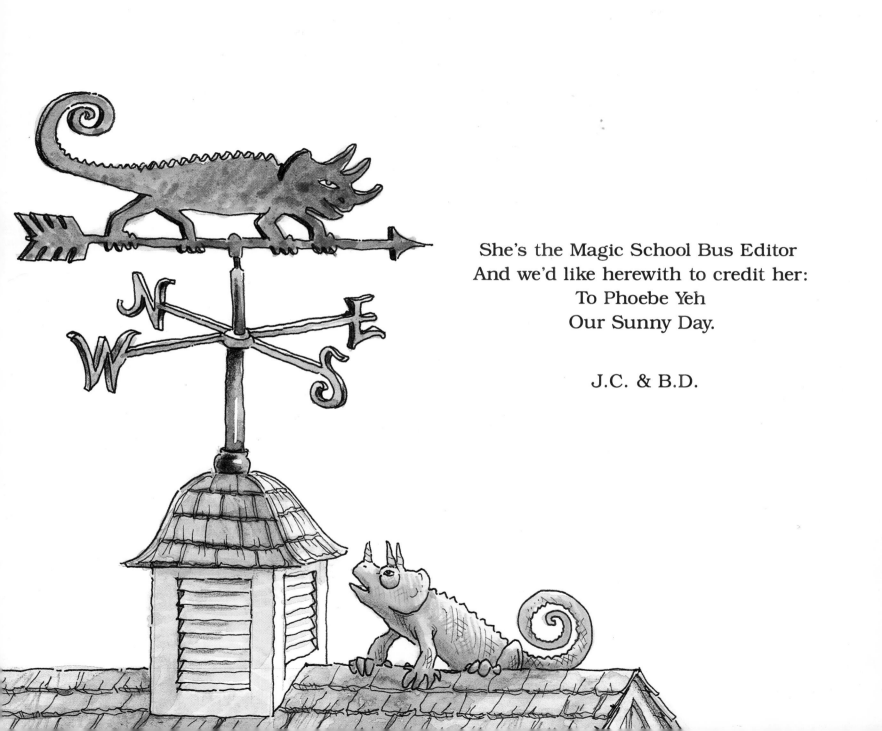

She's the Magic School Bus Editor
And we'd like herewith to credit her:
To Phoebe Yeh
Our Sunny Day.

J.C. & B.D.

Have you heard about our teacher, Ms. Frizzle? Her clothes are wild, her school bus is wacky, and her class trips are weird.
Whenever we study something in her class, we get into it in a *really* big way.

We were learning about weather.
Absolutely everything in our room
was about rain or snow or sun or wind.
Every kid in the class
was doing a weather project.
We were even listening to
weather reports on Ms. Frizzle's radio.

TODAY'S MATH

SPELLING WORDS

Sun	Wind
rain	snow
drizzle	sleet
hail	hurricane
don't	forget
your	umbrella

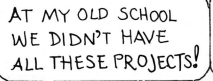

AT MY OLD SCHOOL WE DIDN'T HAVE ALL THESE PROJECTS!

AT MY OLD SCHOOL OUR TEACHER DIDN'T DRESS THAT WAY.

ANEMOMETER measures wind, force and speed.

AND NOW FOR THE WEATHER...

our Snowflakes by Michael and Keesha

Wind Sock

WEATHER FORECASTING MADE EASY

WEATHERMAN

HAIL and HEARTY

RAIN

SNOW

ADVENTURES OF WEATHERMAN

WEATHERMAN FACES THE STORM

WEATHERMAN MEETS SNOWMAN

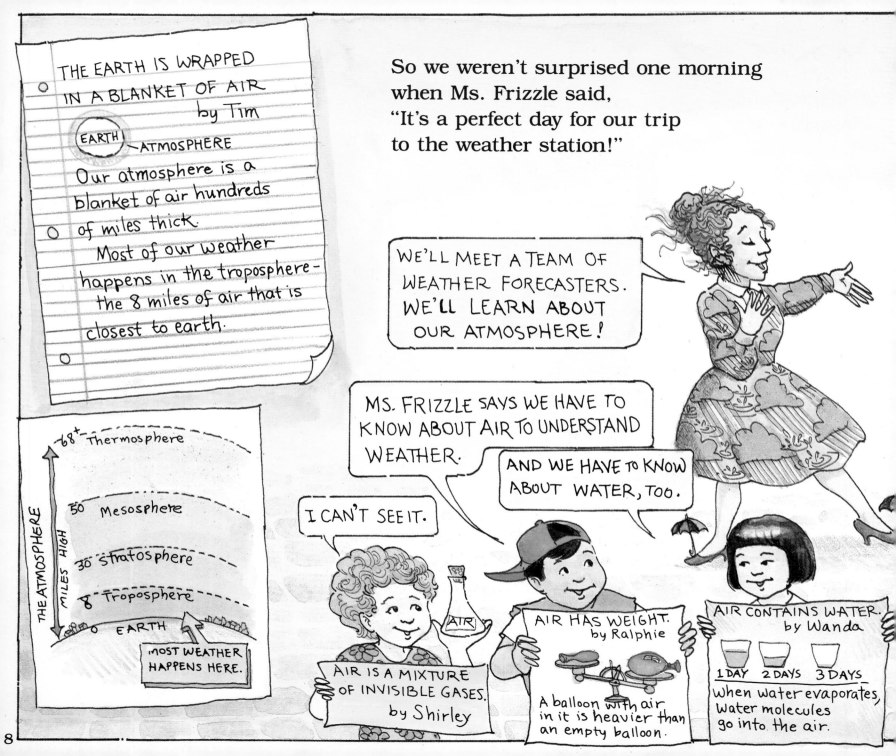

THE EARTH IS WRAPPED IN A BLANKET OF AIR
by Tim

EARTH — ATMOSPHERE

Our atmosphere is a blanket of air hundreds of miles thick.

Most of our weather happens in the troposphere — the 8 miles of air that is closest to earth.

THE ATMOSPHERE

MILES HIGH

68+ Thermosphere

50 Mesosphere

30 Stratosphere

8 Troposphere

0 EARTH

MOST WEATHER HAPPENS HERE.

So we weren't surprised one morning when Ms. Frizzle said, "It's a perfect day for our trip to the weather station!"

WE'LL MEET A TEAM OF WEATHER FORECASTERS. WE'LL LEARN ABOUT OUR ATMOSPHERE!

MS. FRIZZLE SAYS WE HAVE TO KNOW ABOUT AIR TO UNDERSTAND WEATHER.

AND WE HAVE TO KNOW ABOUT WATER, TOO.

I CAN'T SEE IT.

AIR

AIR IS A MIXTURE OF INVISIBLE GASES.
by Shirley

AIR HAS WEIGHT.
by Ralphie

A balloon with air in it is heavier than an empty balloon.

AIR CONTAINS WATER.
by Wanda

1 DAY   2 DAYS   3 DAYS

When water evaporates, water molecules go into the air.

8

9

We rose higher and higher.
Even though hot air was filling the balloon,
the air around us was growing colder.
We had to put on warm jackets.

A WEATHER WORD
by Dorothy Ann

When water <u>condenses</u>, molecules of water vapor join together and make drops of liquid water.

"Warm air rising from earth carries lots of water vapor molecules," Ms. Frizzle continued.
"As the air rises, it cools down. The water condenses in the air and forms clouds."

We drifted into the center of a cloud.
Ms. Frizzle was right — it was *damp* in there.
The cloud was made of tiny water droplets
hanging in the air.

THREE KINDS OF CLOUDS
by Wanda

1. Curly or wispy clouds are called cirrus.

2. Layered clouds are called Stratus.

3. Lumpy or puffy clouds are called cumulus.

WHEN IS THAT TEACHER BRINGING HER CLASS?

NOT TILL LATER.

MUCH LATER...

WHAT KIND OF CLOUDS ARE FORMING AROUND MS. FRIZZLE AND THE KIDS?

WEATHER STATION

Down below, the weather forecasters were standing in the rain.
They didn't see us inside the cloud, but we could hear their voices.
One of them said, "I hope that teacher knows there's a *hurricane watch* in effect."

CHECK OUT MY HURRICANE WATCH, ARNOLD. GET IT? HURRICANE WATCH!!

I'M PRETENDING I CAN'T HEAR....

WHAT IS A HURRICANE?
by Florrie

A hurricane is one of the most violent kinds of storms.

In a hurricane, winds swirl in a circle around the storm's center at 74 miles per hour or more!

HURRICANE SYMBOL

MORE WORDS FROM DOROTHY ANN

A Hurricane Watch means that a hurricane may strike within the next 36 hours.

A Hurricane Warning means that a hurricane is likely to strike within the next 24 hours.

A warning is more urgent than a watch.

WHAT IS THE EQUATOR?
by Carlos

The equator is an imaginary line around the earth's middle. It divides the globe into two equal parts.

EQUATOR

WHY IS IT HOTTER NEAR THE EQUATOR?
by Michael

Because of the way the earth is tilted, the sun's rays almost always shine toward the earth's middle. This means there are no cold winters there.

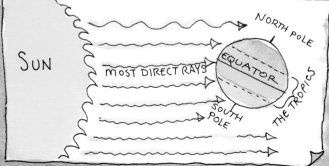

SUN

MOST DIRECT RAYS

EQUATOR

NORTH POLE

SOUTH POLE

THE TROPICS

As usual, Ms. Frizzle paid no attention.
She turned up the fire, and more
hot air rushed into the balloon.
As we rose above the cloud,
the wind started pushing us south.
Before long, we had traveled thousands of miles.
Ms. Frizzle said we were above a tropical ocean
about five hundred miles north of the equator.

WOW! LOOK AT THAT WATER!

WE CAN GO SWIMMING!

AND WINDSURFING!

AND SNORKELING!

Below us, blue-green waves were sparkling.
On a sandy island, palm trees were waving.
It looked like a vacation paradise to us.
But Frizzie said, "Class, we have now arrived
at one of the world's hurricane breeding grounds!"

NEARLY ALL HURRICANES GET STARTED OVER WARM TROPICAL OCEANS, KIDS.

I'VE HEARD THAT HURRICANES ARE DANGEROUS.

SO MS. FRIZZLE IS TAKING US TO ONE.

SHE WOULD!

WHY DO HURRICANES HAVE NAMES?
by Carmen

Often, more than one hurricane is brewing at once. It's easier to keep track of them if they are given names.

Some famous hurricanes:

- Agnes
- Andrew
- Bob
- Elena
- Gilbert
- Gloria
- Ivan
- Katrina

HI BOB!

WHAT'S HAPPENING GLORIA?

WHERE DO HURRICANES BEGIN?
by Tim

In tropical waters near the equator

NORTH AMERICA

EUROPE

ASIA

AFRICA

SOUTH AMERICA

EQUATOR

AUSTRALIA

⟋ Hurricane
← Path of hurricane

19

WHEN IS HURRICANE SEASON?
by Rachel

Most hurricanes begin in the late summer and early fall. That is when tropical oceans are warmest.

The warmer the ocean is, the stronger the hurricane is likely to become.

"Class, remember that as hot air rises from the ocean surface, the water vapor in the air condenses and forms clouds," said the Friz.
Down below, more hot air rushed in from all sides to take the place of the rising air.
In the middle of the rising air,
a column of sinking air formed.
We started sinking with it.

20

"Oh dear," said Ms. Frizzle.
"The balloon must have sprung a leak."
Hot air was rushing out, and the balloon
was plummeting fast.
"Jump ship, class!" shouted the Friz.
She jumped overboard, and we went after her.
Right away, we knew it was a big mistake.

DO ALL TROPICAL STORMS
BECOME HURRICANES?
by Amanda Jane
No. All around the
world, there are more than
100 tropical storms each
year. Only about 60 of them
grow to hurricane strength.
And only a handful
of those ever reach places
where people live.

HURRY UP AND
JUMP, ARNOLD!

I CAN'T LOOK!

FOLLOW
ME, KIDS!

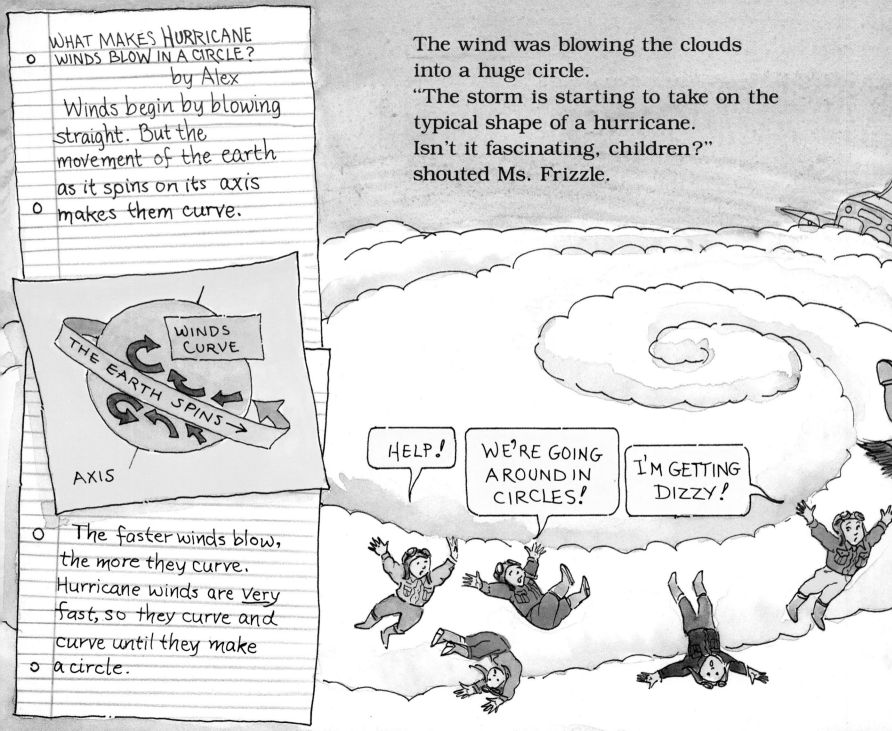

WHAT MAKES HURRICANE WINDS BLOW IN A CIRCLE?
by Alex

Winds begin by blowing straight. But the movement of the earth as it spins on its axis makes them curve.

WINDS CURVE

THE EARTH SPINS →

AXIS

The faster winds blow, the more they curve. Hurricane winds are very fast, so they curve and curve until they make a circle.

The wind was blowing the clouds into a huge circle.
"The storm is starting to take on the typical shape of a hurricane. Isn't it fascinating, children?" shouted Ms. Frizzle.

HELP!

WE'RE GOING AROUND IN CIRCLES!

I'M GETTING DIZZY!

It was more than fascinating.
It was terrifying!
We were caught in the edge of the storm,
blowing around and around in a giant whirlwind.
That whirlwind was a hurricane!

HOW BIG IS A HURRICANE?
by John
Hurricanes are enormous.
Each one is about 10 miles high and 300 to 600 miles wide!

A TYPICAL HURRICANE HAS A LIFE SPAN OF ABOUT 10 DAYS.

LISTENERS— WE'LL BE TELLING YOU ABOUT THE WHOLE HURRICANE.

MAYBE ITS BATTERIES WILL RUN OUT SOON.

Where We Are in the Hurricane

LIGHTNING IS ELECTRICITY
by Ralphie
Clouds become charged with electricity. When the voltage gets high enough, electricity leaps from one place to another. Then we see lightning.

LIGHTNING IS **HOT**!
by Keesha
A lightning bolt reaches a temperature of 50,000° F. That's about five times hotter than the sun's surface!

In the clouds around us,
huge bolts of lightning were flashing.
We thought it was all over for us,
but then we saw the bus again.
It had become a weather plane —
the kind that explores hurricanes.
We tumbled into a rescue chute
and fell onto the plane . . . that is,
the bus . . . er . . . we mean the plane.

All around were columns of air
called hot towers, or chimneys.
They were sucking up more and more
hot moist air from the ocean.
The heat energy from the air
was feeding the storm
and making it stronger.
The plane was shaking
and so were we!

WINDS

WINDS

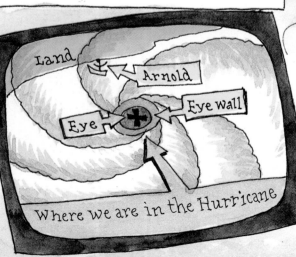

Land

Arnold

Eye wall

Eye

Where we are in the Hurricane

Then suddenly everything was quiet.
"Class, we have entered the eye — or center —
of the hurricane!" announced Ms. Frizzle.
The ocean waves still crashed below
and the winds howled outside,
but in the eye only gentle breezes blew.
Up above, the sky was blue
and the sun was shining.
We relaxed and enjoyed ourselves.

PEACE AND QUIET!

BALMY BREEZES!

A-A-AH!

We flew about thirty miles
across the eye.
Then the Friz called out,
"We will enter the other side
of the eye wall now."
"Don't go!" we cried,
but the plane was already
on its way — back into the
hurricane's fierce wind and rain.

WHY DON'T HURRICANE WINDS
BLOW INTO THE EYE?
by shirley

The winds swirl in toward
the eye of the storm, but
they do not enter it because
they are pushed out by the
same force that pushes
you outward when you
spin around.

HOW HURRICANES TRAVEL
by Wanda

When a hurricane starts, it usually moves slowly—about 10 to 20 miles per hour. As the storm gets farther north, its speed can increase up to 60 miles per hour! Hurricanes can travel hundreds of miles each day.

WHICH PART OF THE HURRICANE IS STRONGEST?
by Florrie

The right front corner is strongest because the whirling winds are circling toward the shore. They add their strength to the winds that move the storm forward.

The entire hurricane was moving across the ocean toward land, and we were going with it! "The right forward corner of the hurricane as you are looking toward land has the strongest wind and rain and the highest ocean waves," shouted the Friz. Naturally, she flew directly into that part.

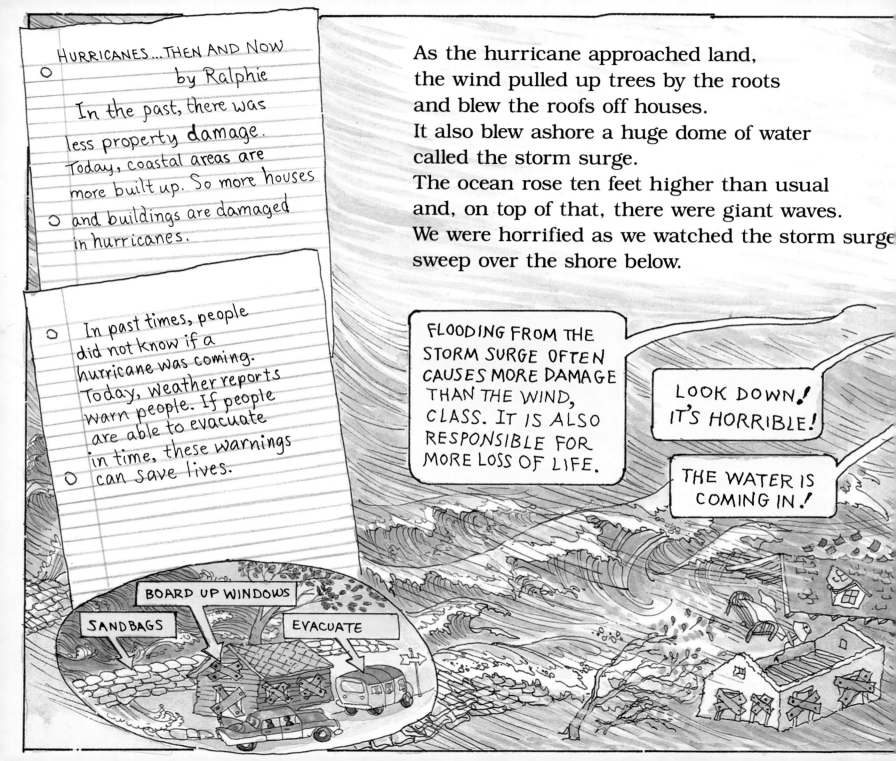

HURRICANES...THEN AND NOW
by Ralphie

In the past, there was less property damage. Today, coastal areas are more built up. So more houses and buildings are damaged in hurricanes.

In past times, people did not know if a hurricane was coming. Today, weather reports warn people. If people are able to evacuate in time, these warnings can save lives.

As the hurricane approached land, the wind pulled up trees by the roots and blew the roofs off houses. It also blew ashore a huge dome of water called the storm surge. The ocean rose ten feet higher than usual and, on top of that, there were giant waves. We were horrified as we watched the storm surge sweep over the shore below.

But that was nothing compared to the horror we felt when we heard the Friz shouting above the sound of roaring water, "We seem to be running out of gas, children!" Sure enough, the plane was dipping lower and lower.

As we fell into the water, we saw Arnold waving to us from a nearby roof.

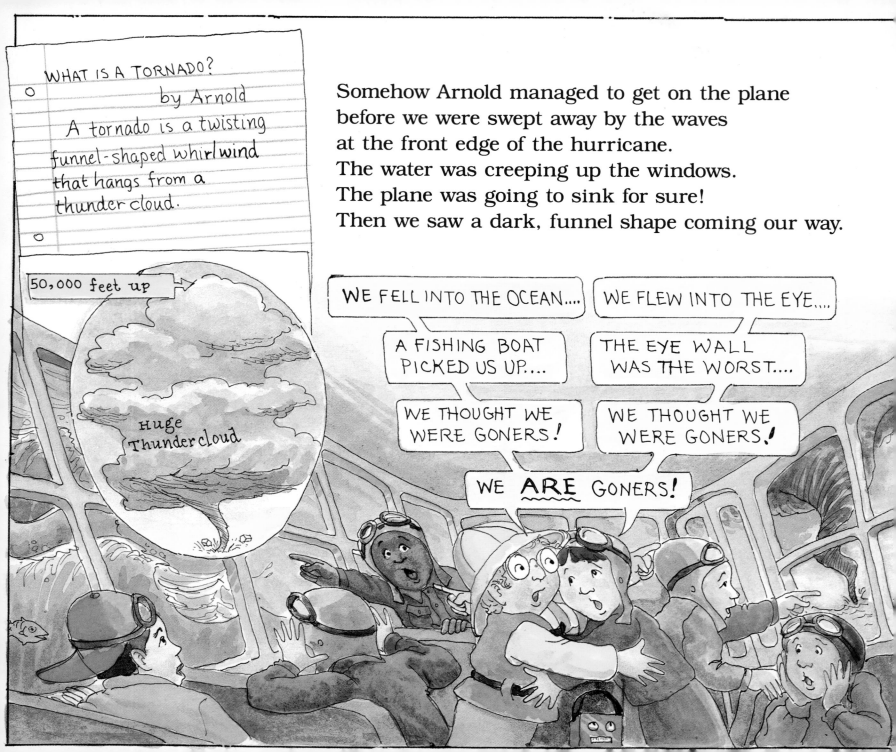

Somehow Arnold managed to get on the plane
before we were swept away by the waves
at the front edge of the hurricane.
The water was creeping up the windows.
The plane was going to sink for sure!
Then we saw a dark, funnel shape coming our way.

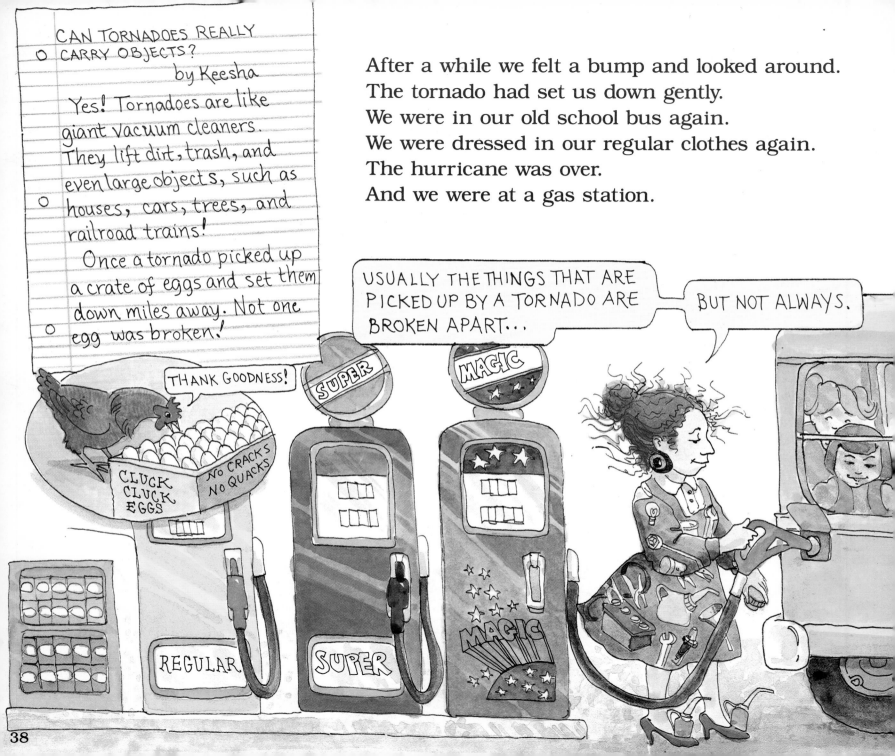

CAN TORNADOES REALLY CARRY OBJECTS?
by Keesha

Yes! Tornadoes are like giant vacuum cleaners. They lift dirt, trash, and even large objects, such as houses, cars, trees, and railroad trains!

Once a tornado picked up a crate of eggs and set them down miles away. Not one egg was broken!

After a while we felt a bump and looked around.
The tornado had set us down gently.
We were in our old school bus again.
We were dressed in our regular clothes again.
The hurricane was over.
And we were at a gas station.

Ms. Frizzle filled up the tank
and drove down the road
as if nothing had happened.
"As I said earlier, class, we are on our way
to visit a weather station," she said.

41

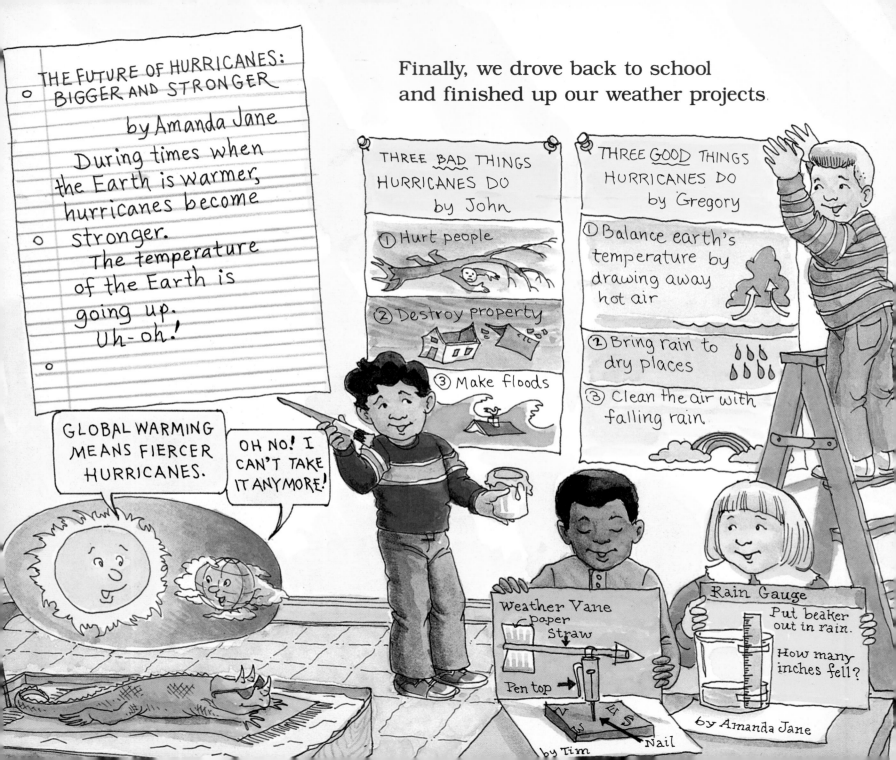

Finally, we drove back to school and finished up our weather projects.

After that trip, we needed some time to relax.
Ms. Frizzle said we could have a party.
We had great games, crazy dancing, and yummy snacks.
And for a while, we didn't even think about
Ms. Frizzle's next class trip!

The Magic School Bus Mail Bag
Letters... We get letters...

U.S. MAIL

To the Magic School Bus Editor:
You should not have said that a school bus could turn into a hot air balloon or a weather plane. That cannot really happen.
Your friend,
Sam

EXOTIC BROOKLYN

FOR SALE

GREETINGS FROM SUNNY EAST ORANGE, N.J.

Dear Joanna,
Radios cannot have conversations with people.
Barbara

TO: JOANNA COLE
AUTHOR
c/o Scholastic Inc.

Dear Joanna and Bruce,
Reading about hurricanes may be fun, but it is <u>no</u> fun to be in one!
I know because my family was in Hurricane ANDREW and it was <u>scary</u>!
— Keith

Dear Bruce,
Radios do not dance.
from Jean

TO: Bruce Degen
ARTIST
c/o Scholastic Inc.

Dear Arnold,
On your trip, the hurricane reached land. But most hurricanes go far out to sea and do not hurt people and property.
Your friend,
Al, the weather scientist

A fishing boat probably would not survive if it were out in a very strong hurricane.
From the Coast Guard

46

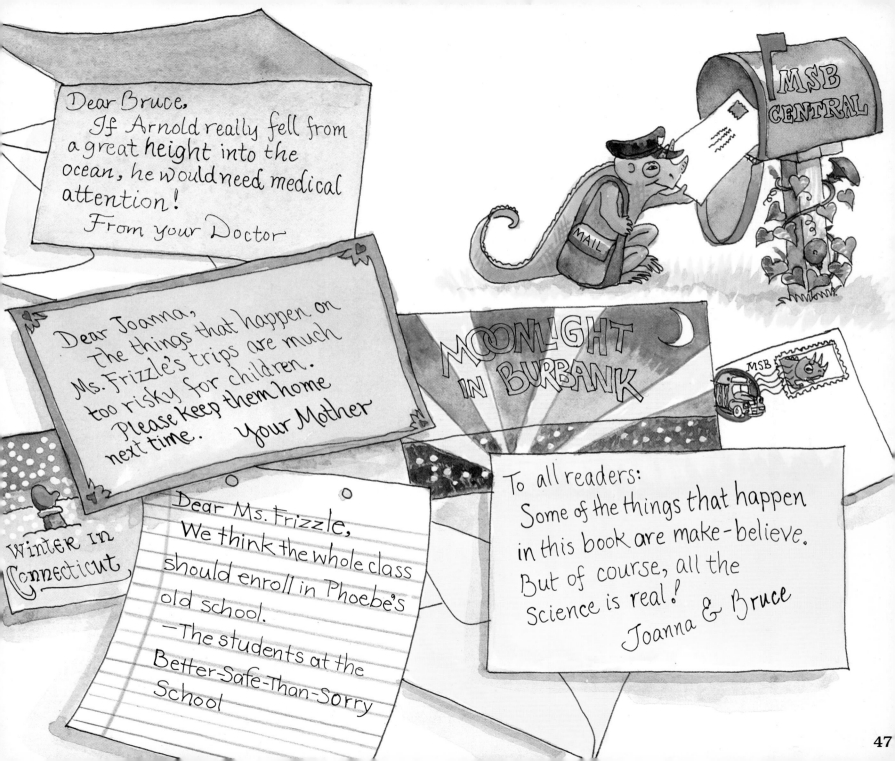

Dear Bruce,
If Arnold really fell from a great **height** into the ocean, he would need medical attention!
From your Doctor

Dear Joanna,
The things that happen on Ms. Frizzle's trips are much too risky for children. Please keep them home next time.
Your Mother

MOONLIGHT IN BURBANK

MSB

Winter in Connecticut

Dear Ms. Frizzle,
We think the whole class should enroll in Phoebe's old school.
—The students at the Better-Safe-Than-Sorry School

To all readers:
Some of the things that happen in this book are make-believe. But of course, all the science is real!
Joanna & Bruce

MSB CENTRAL

MAIL